# Fresh Sounds

COMPANION VOLUME TO 'SOUND OF LIVING WATERS'

compiled by

**BETTY PULKINGHAM**

and

**JEANNE HARPER**

**HODDER AND STOUGHTON**
LONDON SYDNEY AUCKLAND TORONTO

*Processed by Cambridge Music Printing Services, Cambridge.*

# Contents

# Foreword

The flow of new songs as God's Spirit renews his Church today is such that no printing press can hope to keep pace. We offer a second *Sound of Living Waters* under a new title, *Fresh Sounds,* to convey the freshness of many new songs; they have already delighted Christians in different areas, and we trust will be your joy also.

There is in addition an exchange of good hymns from both sides of the Atlantic as in Book 1, set alongside songs of recent popularity such as *Sing to the Lord a new song,* a theme song from an international conference in Rome, and *Moto,* an enthusiastic song from East Africa.

The sections are headed in almost the same way as Book 1. Instead of *Songs for a season* and *Sing a Psalm* we have a liturgical section. In this section alone we find ample illustration of the breadth of the musical taste of the Holy Spirit. Passing from the gentle introit *Allelu* we are invited to *Come and dine* in a rousing American song; a serenely beautiful setting of the *Nunc Dimittis* is included here, and then the *Doxology* from the musical *Come Together.*

We invite you to explore some of the infinite variety and musical resourcefulness of God's creative Spirit and to expect him to use you as a vehicle for his power and praise as you sing, that others may hear and follow on to know for themselves his creativity and blessing.

BETTY PULKINGHAM AND JEANNE HARPER
1976

# Acknowledgments

The editors are tremendously indebted to Mimi Farra for her gifts of precision and musicianship made available to us unreservedly. We wish to thank Gary Miles for his help in proof reading and copying, Mary Felton for her loyal secretarial service to us, Michael Wood for helping us to think clearly about the business procedures involved, and the Watkins family whose home we invaded many times because it afforded us a quiet and encouraging place to work. We are grateful to members of the Community of Celebration at Yeldall Manor in Berkshire, and the Cathedral of the Isles, Cumbrae, Scotland, for their hidden helpfulness in ways too numerous to mention.

Last of all we want to thank the *Fisherfolk* who have sung, taught, experimented with, improved upon and shared many of these songs throughout the Christian world. For indeed it is through their ministry that many in the church have come to hear *fresh sounds.*

SECTION 1

# HALLELUJAH!

## SONGS OF PRAISE AND THANKSGIVING

1.

# 'Sanna

Traditional
*Arr.* Betty Pulkingham

**With fervency of expression**

'San-na,* san-na-ni-na, san-na, san-na, san-na,____

san - na, san-na, san - na, san-na-ni-na,

san - na, san - na, san - na.____ San-____

*This is a shortened form of the word 'hosanna.'

This song may be sung most effectively by voices in four-part harmony, unaccompanied.

## 2. Hail to the Lord's anointed

Based on Psalm 72
James Montgomery

'Yeldall'
Betty Pulkingham

Bright and well-accented

1. Hail to the Lord's a - noint - ed, Great Da - vid's
   Hail in the time ap - point - ed, His reign on
2. He shall come down like show - ers Up - on the
   And love, joy, hope, like flow - ers, Spring in his

great-er Son! ___
earth be - gun! ___ He comes to break op-
fruit-ful earth, ___
path to birth: ___ Be-fore him on the

pres-sion, To set the cap - tive ___ free; ___
moun-tains Shall peace, the her - ald ___ go; ___

To take a - way trans-gres - sion, And rule ____ in ____ e - qui - ty.
And right-eous - ness in foun - tains From hill ____ to ____ val - ley ____ flow.

3. Kings shall bow down before him,
    And gold and incense bring;
   All nations shall adore him,
    His praise all people sing;
   For he shall have dominion
    O'er every sea and shore;
   His kingdom still increasing,
    A kingdom for evermore.

4. O'er every foe victorious,
    He on his throne shall rest;
   From age to age more glorious,
    All blessing and all-blest:
   The tide of time shall never
    His covenant remove;
   His name shall stand for ever,
    His changeless name of love.

## 3. Crown him with many crowns

Matthew Bridges
Godfrey Thring

'Diademata'
George Job Elvey
*Descant by* Betty Pulkingham

**With vigour**

glo - ries now__ we sing, Who died e - ter - nal
him with ma - ny crowns, As thrones be - fore__ him

sing Of him who died for thee, And
known That wrings the hu - man breast, And
sing Who died, and rose on high, Who

life _____ to bring _____ and lives that death may die.
fall, _____ crown him, _____ for he is Lord__ of all.

hail him as thy match-less King Through all e - ter - ni - ty.
takes and bears them for his own, That all in him may rest.
died, e -ter - nal life to bring, And lives that death may die.

4. Crown him of lords the Lord,
    Who over all doth reign,
  Who once on earth, the incarnate Word,
    For ransomed sinners slain,
  Now lives in realms of light,
    Where saints with angels sing
  Their songs before him day and night,
    Their God, Redeemer, King.

5. Crown him the Lord of heav'n,
    Enthroned in worlds above;
  Crown him the King, to whom is giv'n
    The wondrous name of Love.
  Crown him with many crowns,
    As thrones before him fall,
  Crown him, ye kings, with many crowns,
    For he is King of all.

# 4. The God of Abraham praise

Jewish Doxology
*Para.* Thomas Olivers

'Leoni'
*Arr.* Meyer Lyon
*Descant by* Betty Pulkingham

(Descant) 5. The whole tri-umph-ant host give thanks to

1. The God of A-braham praise,
2. He by him-self hath sworn:
3. There dwells the Lord, our King,

Who reigns en-throned a-
I on his oath de-
The Lord, our right-eous-

God on high, _____ 'Hail Fa - - - ther, Son and

bove; An - cient of ev - er - last-ing days, And
pend; I shall, on ea - gle wings up-borne, To
ness, Tri - umph-ant o'er the world and sin, The

Ho - ly— Ghost,' they cry. Hail — A - bra-ham's God and

God of love; To him up-lift your
heav'n as - cend: I shall be-hold his
Prince of peace; On Si - on's sa - cred

mine, we join\_\_\_\_ the heav'n-ly lays, All might and

voice, At whose supreme com - mand, From earth we rise, and
face, I shall his power a - dore, And sing the won-ders
height His king - dom he main - tains, And, glo -rious with his

ma - jes - ty, and\_\_\_\_ end- less praise.. A - - - - - - - - -men.

seek the joys At his right hand. A - - - - - - - - men.
of his grace For - ev - - - er - more.
saints in light, For - ev - - - er reigns.

4. The God who reigns on high
   The great archangels sing,
   And 'Holy, holy, holy', cry,
   Almighty King!
   Who was, and is, the same,
   And evermore shall be:
   Eternal Father, great I AM,
   We worship thee.

5. The whole triumphant host
   Give thanks to God on high;
   'Hail, Father, Son and Holy Ghost!'
   They ever cry;
   Hail, Abraham's God and mine!
   I join the heav'nly lays;
   All might and majesty are thine,
   And endless praise.

## 5. Hallelujah! Gonna sing all about it

Roy Turner
*Arr.* Betty Pulkingham

With a bounce

Hal - le - lu - jah! Gon - na sing all a-bout it. Hal - le-

lu - jah! Gon-na shout all a-bout it. Hal - le - lu - jah! Can't

live with-out it, praise God. (Praise God) Now I'm liv - ing in a

new cre - a - tion, now I'm drink-ing at the well of sal - va - tion.

Now there is no con - dem-na - tion, praise God. (Praise God.)

**6.**

# Hallelujah, my Father

Tim Cullen

**With quiet devotion**

Hal-le - lu - jah, my Fa - ther, for giv-ing us your
Son; send-ing him in to the world to be giv-en up for
men, know - ing we would bruise him and smite him from the
earth. Hal-le - lu - jah, my Fa - - ther, in his
death is my birth. Hal-le - lu - jah, my

Fa - ther,— in his life— is my life.—

## 7. Praise my God with the tambourine

*Adapted from* Judith 16: 1, 13-19
Jerusalem Bible

Diane Davis

**Boldly, with vigour**

Praise my God with the tam - bou - rine; Sing to the Lord with the

cym - - - - - bals. - bals.—

**Verses**

1. I will sing a new song to my God. 'You are
2. 'May your whole cre - a - tion serve you. When you
3. Should the moun - tains top - ple— to min - gle with the waves, should

*Though*      *tumble*      *though*

great,      you are     glo- ri-ous,     won - der-ful - ly___
speak,   things come    in - to being;    no-one can re-sist   your_
rocks melt like wax  be - - - - fore your face,   to

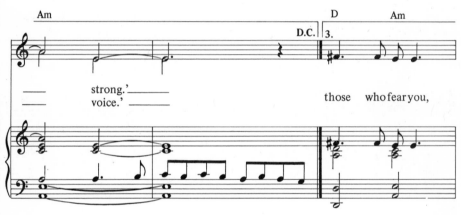

strong.'_____
voice.'_____             those   who fear you,

you would still  be ___   mer - ci - ful.'

will

8. # The dancing heart

Roy Turner
*Arr.* Betty Pulkingham

With joyful abandon

1. Da - vid danced be - fore the Lord, he danced with all his might; his heart was filled with ho - ly joy, his spi - rit was so light. Mi - chal through the win - dow looked, to cri - ti - cise did start, she did - n't know that Da - vid had got a danc - ing heart. Oh, the Ho - ly Ghost will set your feet a - danc - ing! The

(Hal - le - lu - jah)

Ho - ly Ghost will fill you through and through. The

Ho - ly Ghost will set your feet a - danc - ing, and

set your heart a - danc - ing too!

2. David danced before the Lord to magnify his name;
   In God's almighty presence he felt no sense of shame;
   The oil of gladness flowed that day, it quickened every part;
   He hadn't only dancing feet, he had a dancing heart.

3. Out of Egypt long ago the Israelites were led;
   By a mighty miracle they all were kept and fed;
   Through the Red sea they were brought, the waters stood apart,
   And God gave sister Miriam a dance down in her heart.

4. There was a celebration - upon the Red sea shore;
   Timbrels rang, desert sands became a dancing floor;
   The people sang and praised God there, he made the gloom depart,
   And put a dance of love and joy a-deep down in their hearts.

5. The prodigal was far away - wandering out in sin,
   But he came back to father's house and father took him in;
   He put a robe upon his son - the merriment did start,
   The prodigal got dancing shoes to match his dancing heart.

6. The father's house with music rang to welcome home the son;
   Wine was flowing full and free, all misery was gone;
   The elder brother looking on complained it wasn't fair;
   He hadn't got a dancing heart like all the others there.

7. Now many saints are cold and bound by unbelief today,
   They want the blessings of the Lord but worry what men say;
   Oh, let the Lord have full control, from dead traditions part,
   And he will set you free within, you'll have a dancing heart.

9. 

# Now let us sing

Traditional
*Arr.* Betty Pulkingham

**Possible variations:**

Now let us (praise, pray, love.......) *or*
Lift up your (hearts, heads.......)

# 10. Sing praise to the Lord forever

### 'Jacob's Song'

Capo 4 (C)

Jacob Krieger
*Adapted by* Mikel Kennedy

**With strength, briskly**

(Part1) Sing praise to the Lord for - ev - er and ev -
(Part 2) Sing

praise to the Lord for - ev - er and ev -
er.

Call un - to him for hope in sal - va -
er.

tion.
Call un-to him for hope in sal va -

tion. Sing praise, al-le-lu-ia, sing praise, al-le-lu! Sing

praise, al-le-lu-ia, sing praise, al-le-lu!

*last time*

1. Oh, sing praise to our Fa - ther in
2. Oh, sing praise to the Son ___ of
3. Oh, sing praise to the Spi - rit of

**11.**

# Sing, sing alleluia

Nancy Carr Newman

Optional descant for refrain

Sing, sing, sing_____ al-le-lu - ia, sing glo - ry Je - sus Christ.

Sing, sing, sing_____ al-le-lu - ia, be - hold_____ the Lamb of_____ God.__

# 13. Sing to the Lord

Donald Fishel
*Arr.* Betty Pulkingham

**Strongly accented**

Sing to the Lord a new song,

sing to the Lord a new song, sing to the Lord, sing to the Lord a new song.

1. God made the world in sev - en days.
2. God said to Mo - ses, 'Go and set my peo - ple free.
3. Je - sus said to Pe - ter, 'Come on, I'm call - ing you. I
4. Come on my bro - ther, won't you turn to Je - sus now, he

# 13. We will sing to the Lord our God

Richard Gullen

# 14. This is the day of the Lord

Charles High

A good song for unaccompanied singing, using only 'fingertip' clapping (the fingertips of the right hand against the palm of the left.)

*Adapt verses to suit occasion, such as:*

1. This is the (feast.....birthday.....service.....song) of the Lord.
2. We are the people of the Lord.
3. These are the praises of the Lord.

**SECTION 2**

# KNEEL AND ADORE

## SONGS OF WORSHIP

**15.**    # Turn me, O God

Quietly and slowly

Jodi Page

# 16. Jesus, I love you

Kathleen Thomerson

**Simply and softly, not too slow**

love, love you.

Je - sus, I love you, Je - sus, I love you,

Je - sus, I love you, take my life.
1. Life is your
2. Now I have
3. Love reach-es

gift, I give my heart, kneel and a - dore you, and___ I
seen the love of God. He has poured out the Spi - rit of
out both near and far, and so we fol - low where___ you

**1-2.** **3.**

know that Je - sus, I fol - low, Je - sus, I
truth.___ lead us. Je - sus, I love you, Je - sus, I

fol-low,    Je - sus, I   fol-low,    all    my    life.
love you.    Je - sus, I   love you,    take   my    life.

**17.**

# Jesus, Jesus

Anon.
*Arr.* Betty Pulkingham

May be sung as a 2, 3, or 4-part round.

**Slowly, fervently**

Je - sus,   Je - sus,   let me tell you

what I__ know. You have giv - en us your_ spi - rit;

we   love you   so.     so.

# 18. The Shepherd of my soul

Kathleen Thomerson

**Tenderly**

1. I ___ sing to the shep-herd of my soul all the day as he
2. I ___ sing to the shep-herd of my soul all the night for the
3. All my life, O shep-herd of my soul, I will sing with a

leads me through this ___ world. To fol-low him, ___ to tru-ly fol-low
path is clear to ___ him. And when I sleep, ___ he makes a shel-ter
heart that's full of ___ joy. To fol-low you ___ is just to trust that

in his way is to live a life of love.
of his light; when I wake he leads me on.
you will bring all your sheep in-to the fold.

*Refrain*

All I am I of-fer Je - sus, sing - ing praises un-to him.

Oh, my soul, give thanks to Je - sus, for he is your shep-herd-king.

## 19.     Come into his presence

Anon.

**Smoothly, not fast**

Come in - to his pres - ence sing - ing, 'Al - le - lu - ia,'

'Al - le - lu - ia,' 'Al - le - lu - ia.'

*final ending*

*Other verses may be added:*

Come into his presence singing,
    'Jesus is Lord'..........
    'Worthy the Lamb'.......
    'Glory to God'.......

## 20. My song is love unknown

Samuel Crossman

John Ireland

**Fervently, not slow**

1. My song is love un - known, My Sa-viour's love to me;___ Love to the love - less shown, That they might love - - - ly be. O who am I, that for my sake My Lord should take frail flesh and die?

2. He came from his blest throne Sal - va - tion to be - stow;___ But men made strange, and none The longed - for Christ would know: But O, my friend, my friend in - deed, Who at my need his life did spend.

3. Some-times they strew his way And his sweet prais - es sing; ___ Re - sound - ing all the day Ho - san - nas to their King. Then 'Cru - ci - fy!' is all their breath, And for his death they thirst and cry.

4. They rise and needs will have
My dear Lord made away;
A murderer they save,
The Prince of life they slay,
    Yet cheerful he to suff'ring goes,
    That he his foes from thence might free.

5. In life, no house, no home
My Lord on earth might have;
In death, no friendly tomb,
But what a stranger gave.
    What may I say? Heaven was his home;
    But mine the tomb wherein he lay.

6. Here might I stay and sing,
No story so divine;
Never was love, dear King,
Never was grief like thine.
    This is my friend, in whose sweet praise
    I all my days could gladly spend.

## 21. I love the name of Jesus

Capo 3 (D)

Tenderly

Kathleen Thomerson

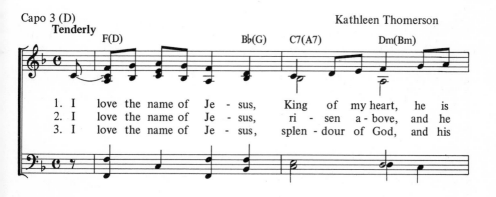

1. I love the name of Je-sus, King of my heart, he is
2. I love the name of Je-sus, ri-sen a-bove, and he
3. I love the name of Je-sus, splen-dour of God, and his

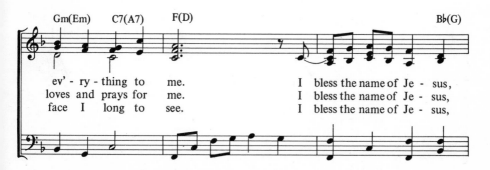

ev'-ry-thing to me.      I bless the name of Je-sus,
loves and prays for me.      I bless the name of Je-sus,
face I long to see.      I bless the name of Je-sus,

# 22.  Blessed be the name

Capo 1 (E)

Anon.
*Arr.* Betty Pulkingham

2. Jesus is the name, Jesus is the name, } *repeat*
   Jesus is the name of the Lord.

3. Worthy to be praised, worthy to be praised, } *repeat*
   Worthy to be praised is the Lord.

**23.**

# Glory

Mimi Farra

Capo 3 (D)

F(D)

2, 3. Sing, _____ oh sing to the Son / Lamb of _____ God,

4. Sing, oh sing to the Word of God, the

F Maj7 (D Maj7)

F +6 (D +6)

Sing, for he is _____ wor - - - thy of _____

Word made flesh in _____ Je - sus _____ Christ.

C7 (A7)

D.S.

D.S.*

D.S.

* Following verse 4 the refrain may be repeated several times, beginning softly, increasing volume and momentum as repetitions occur, and adding the following descant on the final refrain:

*Descant (for soprano solo or a few treble voices)*

Glo - - - ry, glo - - - ry, glo - - - -

- - - - - - ry, glo - ry Je - sus Christ. Glo - - - - -

- - - ry, glo - ry, glo - - - - - - ry, glo - ry Je - sus Christ.

## 24.

# Sweet Jesus

Anon.
*Arr.* Life and Soul Group

Sweet Je - - - - - - - sus, sweet Je - - - - - - - sus, li - ly of the val-ley, bright as the morning

2. How I love him, how I love him,
   Lily of the valley, bright as the morning star.
   How I love him, how I love him,
   He's the God of every nation,
   Bless his name.

3. Jesus loves you.....
4. Sweet Jesus.....

# 25.

# Sweet Jesus

Paul Goodwin
*Arr.* Betty Pulkingham

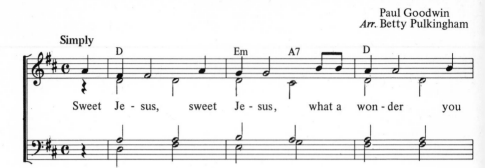

Sweet Je - sus, sweet Je - sus, what a won - der you

are, you are bright - er than the morn - ing star; \_\_\_\_ you are

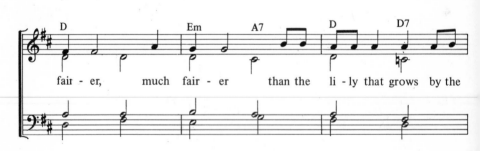

fair - er, much fair - er than the li - ly that grows by the

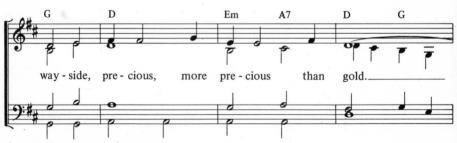

way - side, pre - cious, more pre - cious than gold. \_\_\_\_

You are the rose of Sha-ron, the fair-est of the

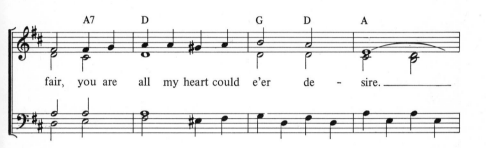

fair, you are all my heart could e'er de - sire.

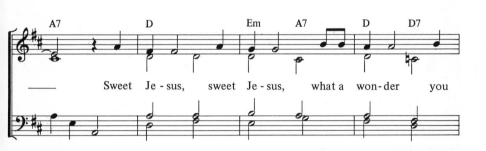

Sweet Je - sus, sweet Je - sus, what a won-der you

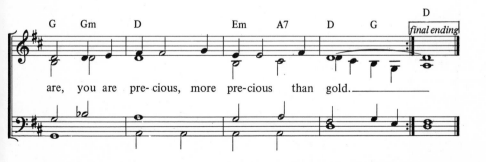

are, you are pre-cious, more pre-cious than gold.

## 26. God gives peace like a river

Anon.
*Arr.* Betty Pulkingham

*Other verses may be added:*
God gives love ..... joy ..... faith ..... hope ..... praise ... *etc.*

*Use these chords if guitar plays alone.

# 27. O worship the Lord in the beauty of holiness

John S.B. Monsell

'Was lebet, was schwebet'

**With breadth and feeling**

1. O wor-ship the Lord in the beau-ty of ho-li-ness, Bow down be-
2. Low at his feet lay thy bur-den of care-ful-ness, High on his
3. Fear not to en-ter his courts in the slen-der-ness, Of the poor

fore him, his glo-ry pro-claim; With gold of o - be-dience and
heart he will bear it for thee, Com-fort thy sor-rows and
wealth thou would'st reck-on as thine; Truth in its beau-ty, and

in-cense of low - li-ness, Kneel and a-dore him, the Lord is his name.
an-swer thy prayer-ful-ness, Guid-ing thy steps as may best for thee be.
love in its ten - der-ness, These are the off'rings to lay on his shrine.

4. These, though we bring them in trembling and fearfulness,
   He will accept for the name that is dear;
   Mornings of joy give for evenings of tearfulness,
   Trust for our trembling, and hope for our fear.

5. O worship the Lord . . . . . . . . *(same as verse 1)*

# 28.

# My Jesus, I love thee

Capo 1 (E)
W. R. Featherston

A. J. Gordon

**Soft and intense**

1. My Jesus, I love thee, I know thou art mine, For
2. I love thee because thou hast first lov-ed me, And
3. I'll love thee in life, I will love thee in death, And

thee all the fol - lies of sin I re - sign. My
pur - chased my par - don on Cal - va-ry's tree. I
praise thee as long as thou lend - est me breath; And

gra - cious Re - deem - er, my Sa - viour art thou:
love thee for wear - ing the thorns on thy brow:
say when the death - dew lies cold on my brow:
If

ev - er I loved thee, my Je - sus, 'tis now.

* Guitar chords and 4-part harmonization not designed to be used together.

4. In mansions of glory and endless delight,
   I'll ever adore thee in heaven so bright;
   I'll sing with the glittering crown on my brow;
   If ever I loved thee, my Jesus, 'tis now.

## 29. Turn your eyes upon Jesus

H. H. Lemmel

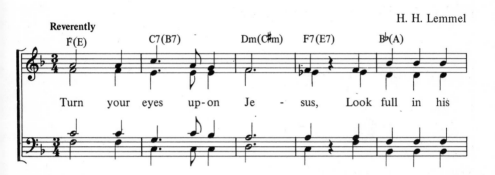

Turn your eyes up-on Je - sus, Look full in his

won-der-ful face; And the things of earth will grow

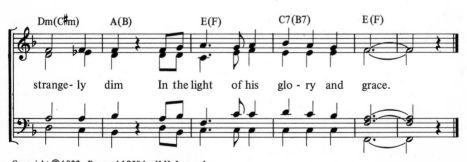

strange-ly dim In the light of his glo - ry and grace.

# 30.    Jesus, the very thought of thee

*Tr.* Edward Caswall

'Windsor'
M. William Damon
*Descant by* Betty Pulkingham

**With awe; not slow**

4. But what to those who find? Ah, this
   Nor tongue nor pen can show;
   The love of Jesus, what it is,
   None but who love him know.

5. Jesus, our only joy be thou,
   As thou our prize wilt be;
   In thee be all our glory now,
   And through eternity.

# 31.  My God, how wonderful thou art

Frederick William Faber

'Windsor'
M. William Damon

1. My God, how wonderful thou art,
   Thy majesty how bright!
   How beautiful thy mercy-seat,
   In depths of burning light!

2. How dread are thine eternal years,
   O everlasting Lord,
   By prostrate spirits day and night
   Incessantly adored!

3. O how I fear thee, living God,
   With deepest tenderest fears,
   And worship thee with trembling hope,
   And penitential tears.

4. Yet I may love thee too, O Lord,
   Almighty as thou art,
   For thou hast stooped to ask of me
   The love of my poor heart.

5. How wonderful, how beautiful,
   The sight of thee must be,
   Thine endless wisdom, boundless power,
   And aweful purity.

SECTION 3

# LITURGICAL SONGS

INTROIT

**32.** # Come and dine

C. B. Widmeyer
*Arr.* Betty Pulkingham

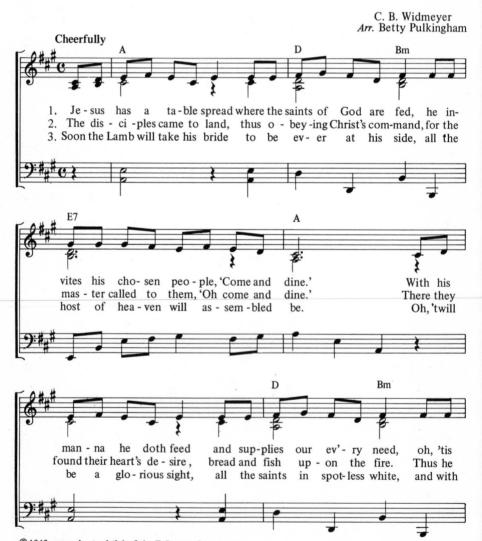

Cheerfully

1. Je-sus has a ta-ble spread where the saints of God are fed, he in-
2. The dis-ci-ples came to land, thus o-bey-ing Christ's com-mand, for the
3. Soon the Lamb will take his bride to be ev-er at his side, all the

vites his cho-sen peo-ple, 'Come and dine.' With his
mas-ter called to them, 'Oh come and dine.' There they
host of hea-ven will as-sem-bled be. Oh, 'twill

man-na he doth feed and sup-plies our ev'-ry need, oh, 'tis
found their heart's de-sire, bread and fish up-on the fire. Thus he
be a glo-rious sight, all the saints in spot-less white, and with

## 33. I will arise

Capo 3 (A)

Mimi Farra

I will a - rise    so    ear - ly in the   morn - ing,  rise to—

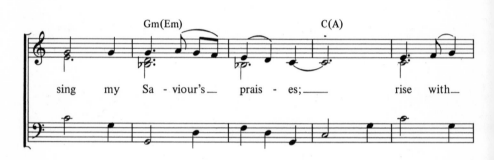

sing    my    Sa - viour's—  prais - es;——        rise with—

joy    in   my    heart—   to   greet the—   Lord    who  gives    me—

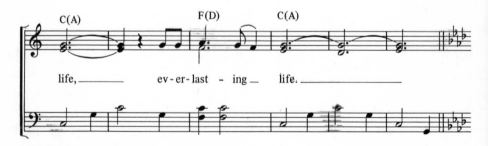

life,———        ev - er - last - ing—  life.———

Lord ____ of __ love. ____

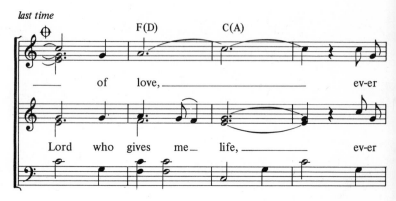

____ of love, ____ ev-er

Lord who gives me __ life, ____ ev-er

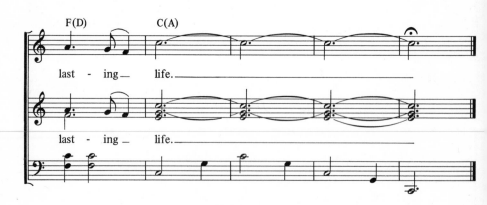

last - ing __ life. ____

last - ing __ life. ____

\* Verse 2 is a musical complement to the refrain, and the
two may be sung together as a final (additional) refrain,
using the ending marked *'last time.'*

# 34.

# Allelu

Mimi Farra

**With a lilt**

1. Come and bless, come and praise, come and praise the liv - ing God.

*Refrain:* Al - le - lu, al - le - lu, al - le - lu - ia, Je - sus Christ.

Al - le - lu, al - le - lu, al - le - lu - ia, Je - sus

Christ.

*final ending*

2. Come and seek, come and find, come and find the living God.
   Allelu, allelu, alleluia, Jesus Christ. *Refrain.*

3. Come and hear, come and know, come and know the living God.
   Allelu, allelu, alleluia, Jesus Christ. *Refrain.*

4. Come and bless, come and praise, come and praise the Word of God;
   Word of God, Word made flesh, alleluia, Jesus Christ. *Refrain.*

*Seasonal verses:*

5. Come behold, come and see, come and see the new-born babe.
   Allelu, allelu, alleluia, Jesus Christ. *Refrain.*

6. Angel choirs sing above, 'Glory to the Son of God!'
   Shepherd folk sing below, 'Allelu, Emmanuel!' *Refrain.*

**35.**

# I trust in thee, O Lord

(Psalm 31)

M. Mc Allister
*Arr.* Jeanne Harper

## 36.

# O magnify the Lord

(Based on Psalm 34)

Capo 5 (Am)

Ruth Wieting

all times, his praise will al - ways_
Lord, _____ and he has freed me__
saints, _____ for those who trust him__
God, _____ to be the bo - dy__

be in my mouth. ⎤
from all my fears. ⎥
lack no good thing. ⎥
of Je - sus Christ. ⎦

O _____

# 37.

# There is a river

### (Psalm 46)

Psalm 46: 4-5

Jonathan Asprey

**Fast, rollicking tempo** *(1 beat to a bar)*

There is a riv - er _____ whose

the ci-ty of God.

God is in the midst of her,—

she shall not be moved;—

the Lord of hosts is

with her.— For

# 38. O give thanks unto the Lord

## (Psalm 136)

Kathleen Thomerson

Joyfully

O give thanks un-to the Lord, for he is good, for his mer - cy en - dur - eth for - ev - er.

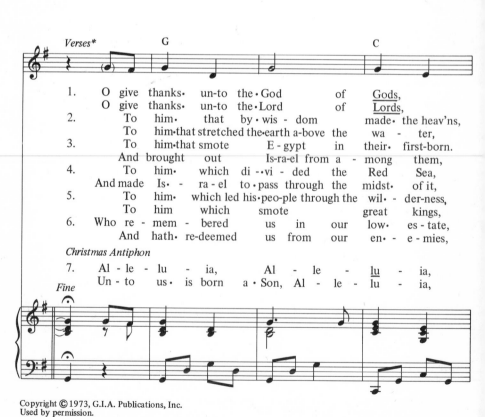

Verses*

1. O give thanks· un-to the·God of Gods,
   O give thanks· un-to the·Lord of Lords,
2. To him· that by·wis - dom made· the heav'ns,
   To him·that stretched the·earth a-bove the wa - ter,
3. To him·that smote E - gypt in their· first-born.
   And brought out Is-ra-el from a - mong them,
4. To him· which di --vi - ded the Red Sea,
   And made Is - ra - el to·pass through the midst· of it,
5. To him· which led his·peo-ple through the wil· - der-ness,
   To him which smote great kings,
6. Who re - mem - bered us in our low· es - tate,
   And hath· re-deemed us from our en· - e - mies,

Christmas Antiphon

7. Al - le - lu - ia, Al - le - lu - ia,
   Un - to us· is born a · Son, Al - le - lu - ia,

Fine

For his mer - cy en - dur - eth for - ev - er.

1. To him who a - lone do - eth great won -
2. To him that made great
3. With a strong hand and with a stretched out
4. But ov - er - threw Fha - roah and all his
5. And gave them land for an her - i -
6. O give thanks un - to the God of hea - - -
7. And he shall rule with e - qui -

Refrain

ders,
lights, For his mer - cy en - dur - eth for - ev - er._____
arm,
host,
tage,
ven,
ty,

D.C.

*1. Underlined syllables are sung on more than one melody note.
 2. A dot (·) shows where to change melody note.

# 39. The song of Simeon
### (Nunc Dimittis)

Luke 2: 29-32

Mimi Farra

Lord, you have ful-filled your word; now let your ser-vant de-part in peace.

1. With my own eyes __ I __ have seen __ the sal-va-tion, which
2. A __ light to re-veal __ you to __ the na-tions, and the

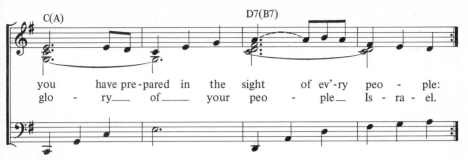

you have pre-pared in the sight of ev'-ry peo - ple:
glo - ry____ of____ your peo - ple____ Is - ra - el.

## 40. My soul doth magnify the Lord

(Magnificat)

Luke 1: 46-47, 49.

Composer and author unknown
*Arr.* Betty Pulkingham

**Gently**

My soul doth mag-ni-fy____ the Lord, and my

spi - rit hath re-joiced in God my sa - viour for____

he that is might-y hath done great things, and ho - ly is his

**41.**
# Jesus, Lamb of God
## (Agnus Dei)

From *'Mass for the King of Glory'*                        Betty Pulkingham

**Slow and sustained**

Je - sus,  Lamb __ of  God, have mer - cy __ on us.  Je - sus,  bear-er of our sins, have mer - cy __ on us.  Je - sus,  re-deem-er of the __ world,  give __ us __ your peace. __ Give  us  your  peace. __ __

The publishers are grateful to the International Consultation on English Texts for the use of their copyright material.

# 42. Calypso Doxology

Thomas Ken
*Verse 2* - Deanna Wheeler

'Jamaica Farewell'
Lord Burgess
*Arr.* Betty Pulkingham

1. Praise God from whom all bless-ings flow, _ praise him
2. Hal - le - lu - jah! Got the vic - to - ry
3. A - men, a - men, a - men, a - men, _ a - men,

all ye crea - tures _ here be - low. _
o - ver Sa - tan and o - ver sin. _
a - men, a - men, a - men, a - men. _

Praise him a - bove, ye _ heav'n - ly host, _ praise him
(7) Je - sus Christ is a - live to - day _ and he
A - men, a - men, a - men, a - men, _ a - men,

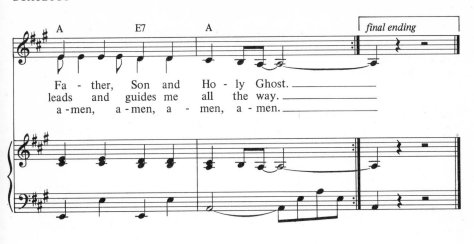

Fa - ther, Son and Ho - ly Ghost. _____
leads and guides me all the way. _____
a - men, a - men, a - men, a - men. _____

43.    # Tallis' Canon

Thomas Tallis
'Evening Hymn'

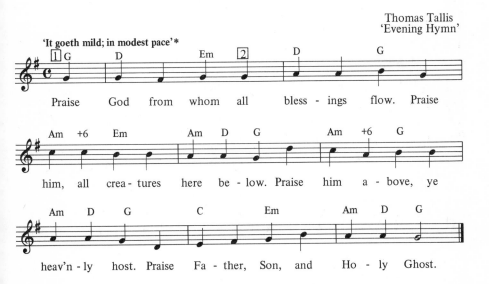

Praise God from whom all bless - ings flow. Praise

him, all crea - tures here be - low. Praise him a - bove, ye

heav'n - ly host. Praise Fa - ther, Son, and Ho - ly Ghost.

Archbishop Parker's Psalter, c. 1567

# 44. Doxology

Thomas Ken

Jimmy Owens

**With movement**

Praise God ____ from whom all bless - ings

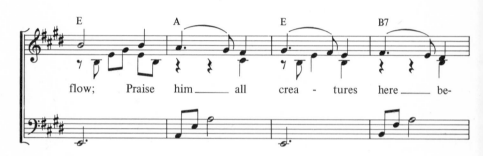

flow; Praise him ____ all crea - tures here ____ be-

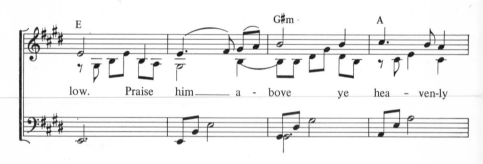

low. Praise him ____ a - bove ye hea - ven-ly

hosts; Praise Fa - ther, Son, and Ho - ly Ghost.

*Optional 4-part setting*

† One very attractive way to sing this song in parts:

First time:  Sopranos begin    Add altos at mid-point*

Second time:  Tenors join    Basses too (at mid-point)*

Third time:  All sing

**45.**

# The Lord's Prayer

Jodi Page

Slow and sustained

Our Fa-ther in hea-ven, _____ hal-lowed be your name. Your king-dom come, your will be done on earth as in hea-ven. _____

Give us to-day our dai-ly bread. For-give us our sins as we for-give those _____ who sin a-

# 49.

# Hallowed be thy name

Traditional
*Arr.* Betty Pulkingham

1. Our _____ Fa - ther who art ___ in ___ hea - ven,
2. On the ___ earth ___ as it is ___ in ___ hea - ven,
3. give us ___ all ___ our ___ tres - pas - ses, _____
4. lead us ___ not ___ to the de - vil to be tempt - ed,
5. thine is the king-dom and the pow- er and the glo - ry,
6. men, a - men, a - men, a - men, _____

Hal - low - ed     be thy     name.

Thy ___
Give ___
As ___
But de-
For -
A-

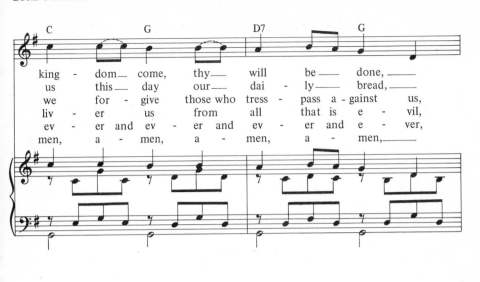

king - dom— come, thy— will be — done, —
us this — day our— dai - ly— bread,—
we for - give those who tress - pass a - gainst us,
liv - er us from all that is e - vil,
ev - er and ev - er and ev - er and e - ver,
men, a - men, a - men, a - men,—

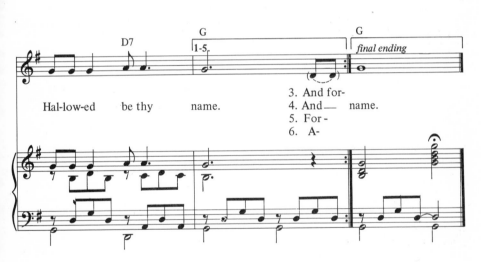

Hal-low-ed be thy name.

3. And for-
4. And— name.
5. For -
6. A-

SECTION 4

# BECOME....

## SONGS OF WHOLENESS AND MATURITY

## 47. The steadfast love of the Lord

Capo 4 (C)

Edith Mc Neill

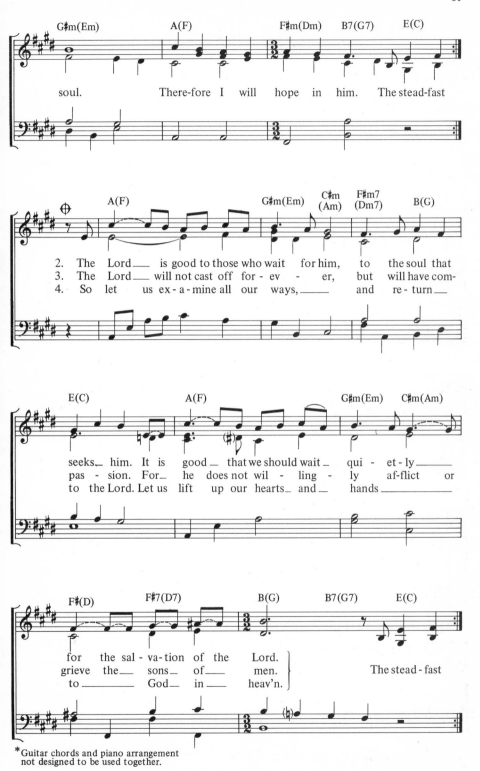

soul.                    There-fore I will hope in him. The stead-fast

2. The Lord— is good to those who wait   for him,   to   the soul that
3. The Lord— will not cast off for - ev - er,   but   will have com-
4. So let   us ex-a-mine all our   ways,___   and   re - turn—

seeks— him. It is   good — that we should wait — qui - et-ly___
pas - sion. For— he does not wil - ling - ly   af-flict   or
to the Lord. Let us lift   up our hearts— and — hands___

for   the sal - va-tion of the   Lord.
grieve   the— sons— of— men.        The stead - fast
to ___ God— in ___ heav'n.

*Guitar chords and piano arrangement
not designed to be used together.

# 48.

# Put on love

Col. 3: 12-16

Jodi Page

**Folk-rock**

will keep our hearts in

per - fect har-mo - ny, _____

if we put _____ on _____

_____ love. _____

## 49.   I heard the voice of Jesus say

Horatius Bonar

'Kingsfold'
Traditional English melody
*Arr.* Betty Pulkingham

1. I— heard the voice of Je - sus say, 'Come un - to me— and
   heard the voice of Je - sus say, 'Be - hold, I free - ly
   heard the voice of Je - sus say, 'I— am this dark world's

rest;       Lay— down, thou wea - ry    one, lay down Thy—
give        The— liv - ing wa - ter;   thirst - y one, Stoop
light;      Look un - to me,    thy    morn shall rise, And—

head up - on— my breast.'     I—— came to Je - sus
down and drink, and live.'      I—— came to Je - sus
all thy day— be bright.'       I—— looked to Je - sus

*The obligato (stems up) may be played by a flute
or by a solo stop on the organ.

## 50. There is power in the blood

*Verses:* Gary Miles
*Refrain:* L. E. Jones

*Verses:* Gary Miles
*Refrain:* L. E. Jones

1. My Je - sus,_____ he saves and heals me, my bo - - - - - - dy, spi - rit, soul. My king and my shep-herd leads me and makes_____ my bo - dy whole.

2. He fills me _____ to o - ver flow - ing, he comes_____ as the dove, My spi - rit and his u - ni - ted. Oh, won - - - - - - drous, pre-cious love.

3. Our Fa - ther,_____ he made and loves us, he gave_____ his on - ly son. We'll see him one day in glo - ry and join_____ the Three in One.

*Refrain*

Oh, there is

power, power, won-der-work-ing power in the

blood of the Lamb. There is power, power,

won-der work-ing power in the pre-cious blood of the Lamb.

# The man of Galilee

Linda Rich
*Arr.* Betty Pulkingham

With an easy swing

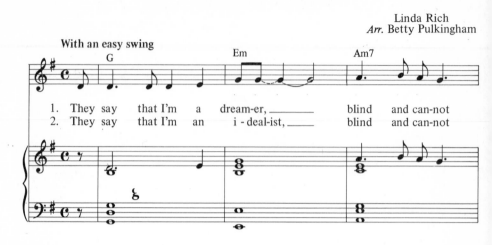

1. They say that I'm a dream-er, _____ blind and can-not
2. They say that I'm an i-deal-ist, _____ blind and can-not

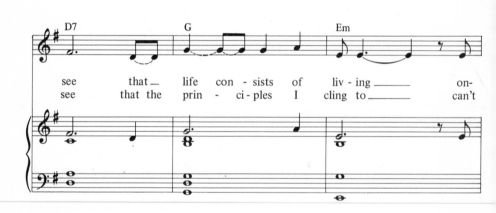

see that — life con-sists of liv-ing _____ on-
see that the prin-ci-ples I cling to _____ can't

ly to earn mon-ey. Well, you know who I
stand re-a-li-ty. Well, I know who you

**52.**

# Wind, wind

Jane and Betsy Clowe

Jane Clowe

**Smooth and sustained**

Wind, wind, blow on me; — wind, wind,

set me free; — wind, wind, my Fa - ther sent the

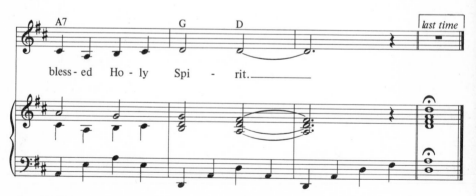

bless - ed Ho - ly Spi - rit. _____

## 53. The fruit of the Spirit

Capo 1 (E)
*Refrain:* Gal. 5: 22-23

Brian Casebow

# 54. By their fruits ye shall know them

Capo 3 (C)
Based on Matt. 7: 16

Jon Wilkes
*Arr.* Betty Pulkingham

With quiet simplicity

Refrain  Eb(C)  Ab(F)  Eb(C)

Can men gath-er grapes from the thorns, _____ or

Fm(Dm)  Bb(G)

(mel.) figs from the thistl - ed stem? _____

Eb(C)  Gm(Em)  Cm(Am)

v.3 (solo) Fa - ther, for - give, _____ they know not what they do;

He that hath ears let him hear, _____

by their fruits ye shall know them.

Verses

1. My friend came to man to show him how to love; his
2. In dark-ness they led him to priests and kings, they
3. They nailed his hands and split his side, they
4. Bro-thers, oh, judge the heart of man-kind, the

(hum)

bless-ing he gave to the meek. But
called him the Lord of the flies.
cast the lots for his clothes.
test is sure and true.

men took his love __ and they called it a lie, his
Spat in his face __ and they crowned him with thorns: _____
The on-ly com-fort _____ they had to give was
Eat of the fruit _____ and sa-vour the taste.

an-swer __ was on-ly this cry: _____
'Hail, the King of the Jews.' _____
vin - - e-gar and __ gall. _____
What does it say _____ to you? _____

by their fruits ye shall know them. _____

## 55. My God
### (A psalm of spring)

Capo 1 (E)
**With warmth**

Nan Pagano

My God makes the flow-ers to bloom. My God sends the rain.— My God sets the rain-bow in the sky,— hears each ba-by when he cries,— and each mo-ther as she sighs,— sent his on-ly Son to die.— Oh, praise him, my God is the on-ly true and liv-ing God and he has made me his child.

1. One day in spring while walk-ing with the Lord,_____
   world and I have gi - ven it to you, ev' - ry
2. When sum-mer heat re-veals the cir-cum-stance of life, _____ the
   comes and all your world is turn-ing brown, the__
3. He spoke a - gain and said,'You are a child of mine,_____ a
   out, 'I see, it's all a gift from thee! Let the

list - 'ning to his word, I heard him say, _____ 'This is my
bur - den and the strife, call on my name._____ Then aut -umn
branch up - on the vine. Bring forth my fruit.'_____ My heart cried

col - our, ev' - ry hue,_____ ev' - ry breeze and drop of dew_ is from my
leaves are fall-ing down and win-ter's cold is all a - round. It's from my
sea-sons have their way, Lord, walk with me through night and day._ It's from your

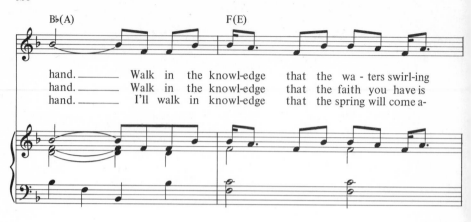

Bb(A)　　　　　　　　　　F(E)

hand. _____ Walk in the knowl-edge that the wa - ters swirl-ing
hand. _____ Walk in the knowl-edge that the faith you have is
hand. _____ I'll walk in knowl-edge that the spring will come a-

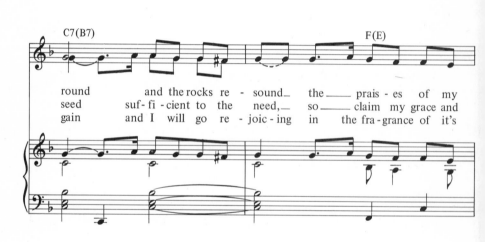

C7(B7)　　　　　　　　　　　　　　　　F(E)

round　　　　and the rocks re - sound_ the _____ prais - es of my
seed　suf - fi - cient to the need,_ so _____ claim my grace and
gain　　and I will go re - joic - ing in the fra - grance of it's

D.S.

name. _____
live!' _____ } My heart cried, my God makes the flow-ers to bloom.
bloom.' _____

# 56. Israel is my vineyard

Isaiah 27 : 2-3
Capo 2 (Em)

Marie Malone

Is - rael is my vine - yard and I, the___ Lord, will tend the fruit - ful___ vines. Ev - 'ry day I'll wa - ter them and day and night I'll watch to keep all en - e - mies a - way. (I'll)

Al - le - lu - ia, al - le - lu - ia, praise the Lord! Al - le - lu - ia, praise his name!

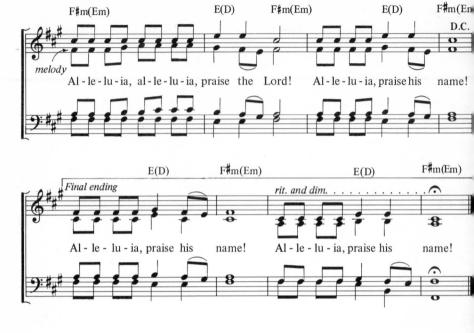

## 57. Thou wilt keep him in perfect peace

Anon.
*Arr.* Paul Beckwith

Descant 3. Though your sins — as scar - let be, Though your —

1. Thou — wilt keep him in per - fect peace, Thou — wilt keep him in
2. Mar - vel not that I say un - to you, Mar - vel not that I
3. Though your sins — as scar - let be, Though your sins — as

sins ___ as scar - let be, Though ___ your

per - fect peace, Thou ___ wilt keep him in
say un - to you, Mar - vel not that I
scar - let be, Though ___ your sins ___ as

sins ___ as scar - let be, They shall ___ be white ___ as snow.

per - fect peace Whose mind is stayed on thee.
say un - to you, Ye must be born a - gain.
scar - let be, They shall be white as snow.

4. If the Son shall make you free,
   If the Son shall make you free,
   If the Son shall make you free,
   Ye shall be free indeed.

5. They that wait upon the Lord,
   They that wait upon the Lord,
   They that wait upon the Lord,
   They shall renew their strength.

6. Whom shall I send and who will go?
   Whom shall I send and who will go?
   Whom shall I send and who will go?
   Here I am, Lord, send me.

SECTION 5

# SONGS OF THE KINGDOM

## THE BODY OF CHRIST

**58.** **The Lord is a great and mighty king**

Diane Davis

and let his prais - es ring. ring.

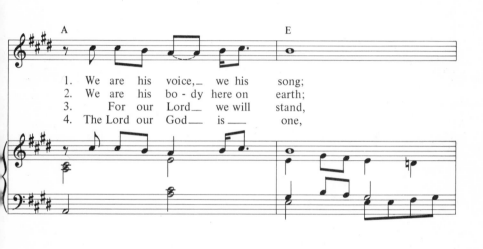

1. We are his voice,_ we his song;
2. We are his bo - dy here on earth;
3. For our Lord_ we will stand,
4. The Lord our God_ is _ one,

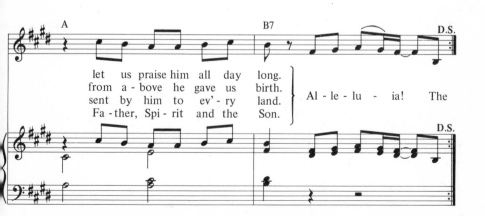

let us praise him all day long.
from a - bove he gave us birth.
sent by him to ev' - ry land.
Fa - ther, Spi - rit and the Son.

Al - le - lu - ia! The

## 59.

# This is the feast

John Ylvisaker
*Arr.* Betty Pulkingham

## 60. Please break this bread, Lord

Jodi Page

108

## 61. Let us break bread together

Traditional
*Arr.* Mimi Farra

**Warmly**

1. Let us break bread to - geth - er, we are one.
   drink wine to - geth - er, we are one.
   praise God to - geth - er, we are one.

Let us break bread to - geth - er, we are one.
Let us drink wine to - geth - er, we are one.
Let us praise God to - geth - er, we are one.

1-3. We are one as we stand with our face to the ris - en

Son. Oh,— Lord, have mer - cy on— us.— 2-3. Let us

us. _____ Lord, have mer-cy on ___ us. ___

## 62. Who are my mother and my brothers?

Charles High

**With deep feeling**

An - y - one who does the will of God,

an - y - one who does the will of God, an - y -

one who does the will of God is ___ my ___ bro - ther,

my sis-ter and mo - - - - - ther. _____

# 63. Triumphant Zion

Philip Doddridge

Gary Miles

**Well-accented, not fast**

1. Tri - um - phant Zi - on, lift thy head From dust and dark - ness and the
2. Put all thy beau - teous gar - ments on, And let thine ex - cel - lence be
3. No more shall foes un - clean in - vade, And fill thy hal - lowed walls with
4. God from on high has heard thy prayer, His hand thy ru - ins shall re-

dead; / Though hum-bled long, / a-
known: / Decked in the robes / of
dread; / No more shall hell's / in-f
pair: / Nor will thy watch - ful

wake at length, / And gird thee with / thy
right - eous - ness, / The world thy glo - ries
sult - ing host / Their vic - t'ry and / thy
mon - arch cease / To guard thee in / e -

Sa - viour's strength.
shall con - fess.
sor - rows boast.
ter - nal peace.

**64.**

# What could be better?

Brian Howard

**Crisp and bright**

1. What could be bet-ter than to
2. What could be bet-ter than to
3. What could be bet-ter than to
4. What could be bet-ter than to

come to dine on this bread and on this wine, the
car-ry the cross that our Lord has giv - en us?
live in love with God's ho - ly cho - sen ones,
fol-low the Lord? In this whole wide world, there's no-thing I'm sure. So

bread of life and the cup of suf-fer-ing, the bo-dy and blood of
Just like his on - ly be - got - ten Son, he's cho - sen us to
liv - ing to-geth - er in u - ni - ty, and out of that life the
fol - low him we shall sure - ly do. Lis-ten he's speak-ing to

Je-sus, our King?_____ I _____ be - - - -
car - ry one._____ I _____ be - - - -
world to feed?_____ I _____ be - - - -
me and you._____ I _____ be - - - -

lieve _____ he's o-pened our eyes_ to real-ly see there's
lieve _____ he's o-pened our eyes_ to real-ly see there's
lieve _____ he's o-pened our eyes_ to real-ly see there's
lieve _____ he's o-pened our eyes_ to real-ly see there's

noth - ing___ bet-ter _____ than to come to dine_ in u - ni - ty.
noth - ing___ bet-ter _____ than to car-ry the cross_ in u - ni - ty.
noth - ing___ bet-ter _____ than to live to-geth-er in u - ni - ty.
noth - ing___ bet-ter _____ than to fol-low the Lord in u - ni - ty.

# 65. Guide me, O thou great Jehovah

William Williams

'Cwm Rhondda'
John Hughes

**Majestically**

1. Guide me, O thou great Je - ho - vah, Pil - grim through this
2. O - pen thou the crys - tal foun - tain Whence the heal - ing
3. When I tread the verge of Jor - dan Bid my anx - ious

bar - ren land; I am weak, but thou art might - y
stream doth flow; Let the fie - ry, cloud - y pil - lar
fears sub - side; Death of death, and hell's des - truc - tion,

Hold me with thy pow'r - ful hand: Bread of hea - ven,
Lead me all my jour - ney through: Strong de - liv - 'rer,
Land me safe on Ca - naan's side: Songs of prais - es,

Bread of hea - ven, Feed me now and ev - er -
Strong de - liv - 'rer, Be thou still my strength and
Songs of prais - es, I will ev - er give to

By permission of Dilys S. Webb.

more,                Feed   me  now__ and__  ev - er - more.
shield,              Be    thou still __ my__ strength and   shield.
thee,                I    will  ev - er__  give    to    thee.

## 66.    God of grace and God of glory

Harry Emerson Fosdick

'Cwm Rhondda'
John Hughes

1.    God of grace and God of glory,
On thy people pour thy power;
Crown thine ancient Church's story;
Bring her bud to glorious flower.
   Grant us wisdom, grant us courage,
   For the facing of this hour. *(repeat)*

2.    Lo! the hosts of evil round us
Scorn thy Christ, assail his ways!
From the fears that long have bound us
Free our hearts to faith and praise:
   Grant us wisdom, grant us courage,
   For the living of these days. *(repeat)*

3.    Cure thy children's warring madness,
Bend our pride to thy control;
Shame our wanton, selfish gladness,
Rich in things and poor in soul.
   Grant us wisdom, grant us courage,
   Lest we miss thy kingdom's goal. *(repeat)*

4.    Set our feet on lofty places;
Gird our lives that they may be
Armored with all Christ-like graces
In the fight to set men free.
   Grant us wisdom, grant us courage,
   That we fail not man nor thee. *(repeat)*

# God, make us your family

Capo 3 (A)

Tim Whipple

With pulsating rhythm

*Refrain*

Your king - dom come, your will—— be done, now that we have be - come your sons. Let the prayer of our hearts dail - y — be: God, make us your fam - - - i - ly.—— The

1. eyes of the blind shall be o - pen'd; —— the
2. ran - som'd of the Lord shall re - turn; —— the
3. na - tions will— see— their shame; —— the

*Optional refrain for Christmastide:*
Laude, Lauda, Laude, Lauda. } *repeat.*
Gloria Emmanuel.

## 68.

# Once no people

*Based on* 1 Peter 2: 9-10
Maggie Durran

Betty Pulkingham

**Bold, well-accented**
*Refrain*

For we are a cho-sen race, a roy-al priest-hood, ho-ly na-tion. Once no peo-ple, now God's peo-ple, pro-claim - - ing his mar - - - vel-lous light.

1. Sing the songs of faith - ful Zi - on,
2. Dance the steps of joy - ful Zi - on,
3. Taste the fruit of peace - ful val - leys,
4. We will serve through trib - u - la - - - tion,

we are the stars and the grains of sand.
cym-bals harps and tam - bour-ines.
sip of the wine and eat the bread.
we will fol - low to the cross.

Through our faith we are made glo - - ri - ous;
Blow the trum - pet, sound the glo - - - ry
Know the shep - herd who is guid - - -ing,
Know the death and pain of suf - - fer - ing;

we     are     sons     of     A - bra - ham. _____
in      the     pres - ence     of     the     Lord. _____
the Lord, the     Lamb_____     of     God. _____
God wipes the     tears____     from our     eyes. _____

Now     God's

light _____

peo - ple     pro - claim - - - - ing his     mar - - - - vel-lous

light. _____

**69.**

# Comfort ye

Clint Taylor
*Arr.* Betty Pulkingham

**Gently**
*Refrain*

Com-fort ye,— com-fort ye,— my peo - ple.—

Thus saith the Lord.— *Fine*

1. Bear each oth - er up in your times of trou - ble strength-en your-
2. Love— one an - oth - er as I have loved you, ev' - ry - thing—
3. Bless— the— Lord for— his great mer - cy, es- pe-cial-ly for his

*D.C.*

selves in your times of— peace.—
else will— fall in - to place.—
Son— Je - sus — Christ.—

4. By my spirit you have great power
   which enables you to do my work.

## 70.

# Wherever two or more

**Smoothly and simply**

Brian Howard

SECTION 6

# SUFFER - REIGN

## SONGS OF FAITH AND VICTORY

71.

# In the name of Jesus

Anon.
*Arr.* Betty Pulkingham

In the name of Je - sus, in the name of Je - sus

we have the vic - to - ry.

In the name of Je - sus, In the name of Je - sus

# Fight the good fight

**72.**

'Old Clarendonian'
Olwen Wonnacott

John S. B. Monsell

**With vigour**

1. Fight the good fight with all thy— might,
2. Run the straight race through God's good— grace,
3. Cast care a - side,——— lean on thy guide,

Christ is thy strength and Christ thy right; Lay hold on life, and
Lift up thine eyes and seek his face; Life with its way be-
His bound-less mer - cy will pro - vide; Trust, and thy trust - ing

it shall be thy joy— and crown e - ter - nal-ly.
fore us lies,—— Christ is the path and Christ the prize.
soul shall prove— Christ is its life and Christ its love.

4. Faint not, nor fear, his arms are near;
   He changeth not, and thou art dear;
   Only believe, and thou shalt see
   That Christ is all in all to thee.

# 73.     Jesus is a-drivin' out Satan

Capo 3 (Am)

Mary Ackroyd
*Arr.* Betty Pulkingham

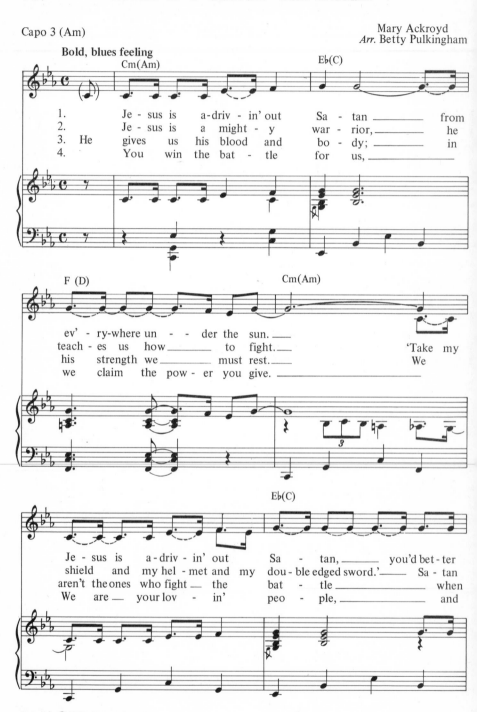

Bold, blues feeling

1. Je-sus is a-driv-in' out Sa - tan from ev'-ry-where un - - der the sun. Je-sus is a-driv-in' out Sa - tan, you'd bet-ter
2. Je-sus is a might-y war-rior, he teach-es us how to fight. 'Take my shield and my hel-met and my dou-ble edged sword.' Sa - tan
3. He gives us his blood and bo-dy; in his strength we must rest. We aren't the ones who fight the bat - tle when
4. You win the bat-tle for us, we claim the pow-er you give. We are your lov-in' peo - ple, and

# 74. Faith is the victory

*Refrain:* John Yates
*Verses:* Betty Pulkingham

*Refrain:* Ira Sankey
*Verses:* Betty Pulkingham

With zest and buoyancy

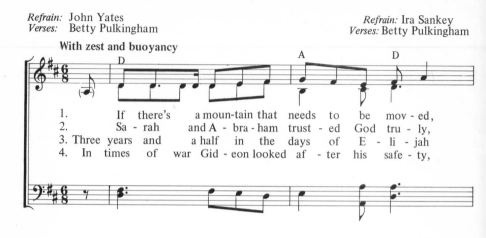

1. If there's a moun-tain that needs to be mov-ed,
2. Sa - rah and A - bra - ham trust - ed God tru - ly,
3. Three years and a half in the days of E - li - jah
4. In times of war Gid - eon looked af - ter his safe - ty,

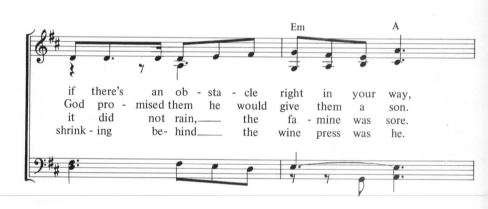

if there's an ob - sta - cle right in your way,
God pro - mised them he would give them a son.
it did not rain, the fa - mine was sore.
shrink - ing be - hind the wine press was he.

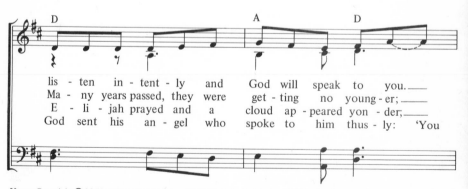

lis - ten in - tent - ly and God will speak to you.
Ma - ny years passed, they were get - ting no young - er;
E - li - jah prayed and a cloud ap - peared yon - der;
God sent his an - gel who spoke to him thus - ly: 'You

Em   A7   D

Trust and o - bey___ him, come___ what may.___
noth -ing's im - pos-si -ble, I - saac did come.___
he thanked___ God and it start - ed to pour!___
va - liant and might-y man, God is with thee.'___

*Refrain*
D                    A                              D

Faith___ is the vic - to-ry. Faith___ is the vic - to-ry.

G          D              A7   D

Oh, glo-ri -ous vic - to-ry that o - ver-comes the world.___

## 75. When I survey the wondrous cross

Isaac Watts

Mikel Kennedy

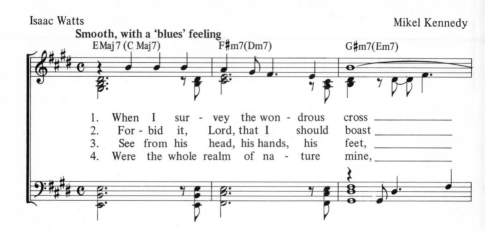

1. When I sur - vey the won - drous cross ____
2. For - bid it, Lord, that I should boast ____
3. See from his head, his hands, his feet, ____
4. Were the whole realm of na - ture mine, ____

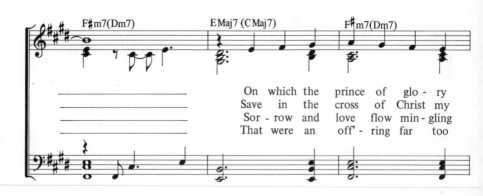

On which the prince of glo - ry
Save in the cross of Christ my
Sor - row and love flow min - gling
That were an off' - ring far too

died, ____ My rich - est
God; ____ All the vain
down; ____ Did e'er such
small; ____ Love so a-

F#m7(Dm7)    G#m7(Em7)    F#m7(Dm7)

gain _____ I count but loss, _____
things _____ that charm me most, _____
love _____ and sor - - row meet, _____
maz - - ing, so di - vine, _____

A(F)    Am7(Fm7)    E Maj7 (C Maj7)

And pour con - tempt on all my pride. _____
I sac - ri - fice them to his blood. _____
Or thorns com - pose so rich a crown. _____
De-mands my soul, my life, my all. _____

F#m7(Dm7)    G#m7(Em7)    F#m7(Dm7)
             1, 2, 3.

E Maj7 (C Maj7)

*Final ending*

*Rit. and dim.* ...............................

## 76. I am persuaded

Romans 8: 38-39

Joan Hettenhouser
*Arr.* Betty Pulkingham

height, nor depth, nor an-y oth-er crea-ture shall be

a - ble to sep-a-rate__ us from the love__ of God,

which is in_____ Christ Je-sus our Lord._____

r.h.

1.

2.

Praise God!

## 77. On Jordan's stormy banks

Samuel Stennett

Traditional
*Arr.* Betty Pulkingham

**Wistful, not too slow**

1. On Jor - dan's storm - y banks I stand and cast a wish - ful eye to Ca - naan's fair and hap - py land where my pos - ses - sions lie.

2. When shall I reach that hap - py place and be for - ev - er blest? When shall I see my Fa - ther's face, and in his bo - som rest?

I am

**Brightly, a little faster**

bound for the pro - mised land, I am

bound for the pro - mised land.

*original tempo*

O who will come and

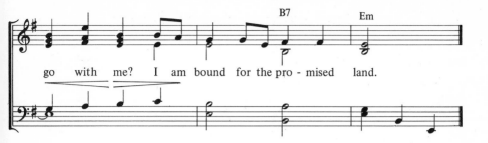

go with me? I am bound for the pro - mised land.

'On Jordan's stormy banks' and 'Come go with me to that land' (the song that follows)
create an unusual medley. Musically, they form a startling contrast; thematically, they
make an interesting progression of thought.

## 78. Come go with me to that land

Traditional
*Arr.* Betty Pulkingham

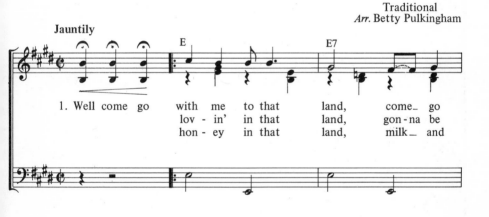

Jauntily

1. Well come go with me to that land, come go
   lov - in' in that land, gon - na be
   hon - ey in that land, milk and

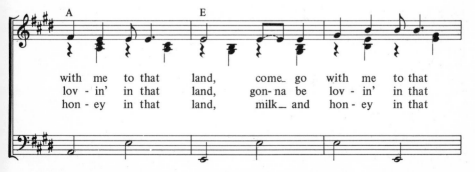

with me to that land, come go with me to that
lov - in' in that land, gon - na be lov - in' in that
hon - ey in that land, milk and hon - ey in that

Other verses may be added:
Gonna meet Jesus in that land ....... Be singin' and dancin' in that land .......
Don't you know heaven is that land?..... etc.

# 79. He is my everything

Capo 1 (E)

Composer and author
unknown
*Arr.* Betty Pulkingham

## 80. There's no greater name

Capo 1 (G)

Michael Baughan

**With a good swing-fairly fast**

1. There's no great - er name than Je - sus,
2. In our minds by faith pro fess - ing,

Name of him who came to save us,
In our hearts by in ward bless - ing,

In that sav ing name of Je - sus
On our tongues by words con-

*2nd. time*

Ev' - ry knee— should bow. _____

Let ev'-ry-thing that is 'neath the ground, Let ev'-ry-

thing in the world a-round, Let ev'-ry-thing that's

high o'er the sky Bow at Je-sus' name.___

___ fess-ing Je-sus Christ is Lord!___

SECTION 7

# COME AS CHILDREN

## SONGS FOR CHILDREN OF ALL AGES

81.     # I am so glad that Jesus loves me

Philipp Bliss
*Arr.* Betty Pulkingham

This is the dear - est, that Je - sus loves me.
When I re - mem - ber that Je - sus loves me.
O what a won - der that Je - sus loves me.

*Refrain*

I am so glad that Je - sus loves me,

Je - sus loves me, Je - sus loves me. I am so glad that

Je - sus loves me, Je - sus loves ev - en me.

## 82. (Someone), Jesus loves you

Anon.
*Arr.* Betty Pulkingham

# 83.

# Jesus loves Kristi*

### (to Kristi)

Capo 1 (E)

Ann House

*As a lullaby*

Je - sus, Je-sus loves *(name).* Yes, he does, yes, he does.

Je - sus, Je-sus loves *(name).* Yes, he does, yes, he does.

Je - sus, Je-sus loves *(name).* Yes, he does, yes, he does.

And he wants *(name)* to love him too._____

* In 1971 Kristi, age 4, went home to her heavenly Father. This song, composed by her mother shortly before her death, was a gift to Kristi, and now it belongs to the whole world.

## 84.

# On tiptoe

Capo 4 (C)
*Verses:* Maggie Durran
*Refrain:* Romans 8: 19
*Philips Translation*

Jodi Page
*Arr.* Betty Pulkingham

Gracefully

1. I
2. I
3. If
4. My

walk with you, my child-ren,     through val - leys filled with gloom;     in
made the mot-tled stickle-back     to    hide in cry - stal streams,     the
life were filled with bub-bles,     they'd glis - ten and they'd burst;     if
love for you, my child-ren,     puts    rain-bows in your hand,

e - choes of the star - light __ and     sha-dows of the moon.     In the
star - ing owl to scan the night, the     can-dle's gen - tle beams;     I __
life were filled with jew - els __     they'd line    a    rich man's purse;     but _
born of cloud-ed sor - rows in    a     sun-burst morn-ing land;     they

whisp-ers of the night-wind are gen-tle words for you to
made the sil-ly cam-el to roam the des-ert sand, but
life is filled with wa-ter that flows from depths of love,
arch a-bove the smi-ling eyes where tears can still be seen, and a-

touch you and as-sure you it's my world you're walk-in'
you I made, my child-ren, to walk and hold my
flows to fill your wear-i-ness with bless - - ing from a-
dorn with gen-tle tremb-ling touch the bride who is my

through.
hand.
bove.
own.

*Refrain*

And all cre-a-tion's strain-ing on

tip-toe just to see _____ the sons of God

come_ in-to their own. own.

## 85.   I sing a song of the saints of God

Lesbia Scott

'Grand Isle'
John Henry Hopkins

**In sturdy march time**

1. I sing a song of the saints of God,____ Pa-tient and brave and
2. They loved their Lord so__ dear, so dear, And__ his love_ made them
3. They lived not on-ly in a - ges past, There are hun-dreds of thou-sands

true,        Who — toiled   and — fought   and — lived    and    died    For the
strong;      And they  fol - lowed the right,   for ___   Je - sus'   sake,    The —
still,       The — world   is ___ bright   with the   joy - ous   saints    Who —

Lord     they — loved   and     knew.        And —   one    was   a   doc - tor, and
whole    of their good  lives   long.        And ___  one    was   a   sol - dier, and
love     to do Je - sus'        will.        You can  meet   them in schools, or   in

one    was a queen,   And —  one   was a shep-herd-ess   on     the — green: They were
one    was a priest,  And —  one   was — slain   by a    fierce  wild — beast: And there's
lanes  or at sea,     In ___ church or  in trains, or in  shops   or  at tea,   For the

all    of them saints of ___  God   and I mean, God    help - ing, to  be   one    too.
not    a - ny rea - son, ___  no,  not the least, Why   I shouldn't  be   one    too.
saints of   God   are just folk  like — me,  And   I  mean to be   one    too.

# 86.

# Knock, knock

'Ask and it shall be given you'

*Based on* Luke 11: 9-13

Betty Pulkingham

**Playfully**

Ask, and it shall be giv-en you. Seek, and ye shall find.___ If you knock, knock, knock, the door will o-pen un-to you ev'-ry time.

1. If a son shall
2. If a son shall
3. If a son shall

ask his fa-ther___ for a piece of bread,
ask his fa-ther___ for a lit-tle fish,
ask his fa-ther for an egg___ o-ver light,

will that fa - ther give his__ son__ a stone in - stead?
will that fa - ther give him a ser - pent in his dish?
will that fa - ther give him a scor-pi - on that can bite?

Verse 4.

Smoothly

4. If ye then, be - ing e - vil, know how to give good things,

How much more your lov - ing hea-ven-ly Fa - ther brings! Your

lov - ing hea-ven-ly Fa - ther brings the best gift of all! He

gives the Ho - ly Spi - rit un - to them that call on him.__

## 87. Pullin' the weeds, Lord *

Max Dyer

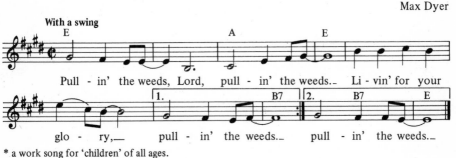

Pull - in' the weeds, Lord, pull - in' the weeds.__ Li - vin' for your

glo - ry,__ pull - in' the weeds.__ pull - in' the weeds.__

* a work song for 'children' of all ages.

*Other suggested verses:*

Sweepin' the floor, Lord.......
Goin' to school (church, bed, *etc!*), Lord.......
Singin' this song, Lord.......

## 88. One, two, three, Jesus loves me

Lisa Mazak
*(age 9)*

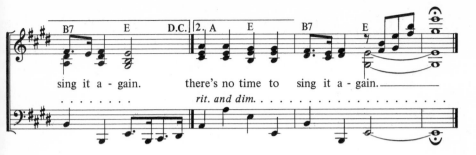

sing it a - gain.   there's no time to   sing it a - gain.

*rit. and dim.*

89.

# Put on your boots

Sherrell Prebble

**Western Americana**

1. Come with me___ to a land where peo – ple are
2. land for now,___ a land where your spi - rit can
3. There you will find___ ach - ing souls___ re-

free,___ where the lambs and the wolves roam to-
live,___ and eat the bread___ of___
vived,___ when the lead - er of___ that

geth - er through the coun - try. _____ They
life that makes____ you whole._____
land____ pass - es by. _____ The

say that a child can ride on a li - on's ____
When you're thirs - ty and you want _____ a
lone - ly peo - ple find____ fel - - low-

back, _____ and not one man____ steals
drink, _____ they have__ liv - ing
ship, _____ and there is plen - ty of

food _ from his bro - ther's shack. _____ So
wa - ter _____ for your souls. _____
heal - ing _____ for the sick. _____

put on your boots, let's get on the road. There's

just not that much time, _____ you know.

know. 2. It's a

## 90. Jesus took my burdens

Anon.
*Arr.* Betty Pulkingham

**Happily**

1. Je-sus took my bur-dens and he rolled them in the sea,
2. Now I am hap-py, hap-py as can be,

rolled them in the sea, rolled them in the sea.
hap-py as can be, hap-py as can be,

Je-sus took my bur-dens and he rolled them in the sea,
Now I am hap-py, hap-py as can be,

nev-er to re-mem-ber an-y-more.
nev-er to re-mem-ber an-y-more.

*'Jesus took my burdens'* may be sung in sequence with the following song.

# I must have Jesus

**91.**

Anon.
*Arr.* Betty Pulkingham

1. I must have Je - sus in my whole life. I must have Je - sus in my life. In my walk-ing, in my talk-ing, in my sleep-ing, in my wak-ing, must have Je - sus in my life.

2. I have Christ Jesus in my whole life.
I have Christ Jesus in my life.
In my walking, in my talking,
In my sleeping, in my waking,
Have Christ Jesus in my life.

## 92. I'm not alone

Diane Davis

walk-ing down the road,
I can trust in him,
I will walk with him,

in ___ class, at
call on his name and
prais-ing him and

work, or at play,
watch him_ move,
bless-ing his name,

he's with me, he loves me wher - ev - er I

go.

go.

he's

with me, he loves me wher - ev - - - - - - - -

er I go.

## 93. Put on the whole armour of God

'The spiritual war'

Ephesians 6: 10-17

Shirley Lewis Brown

**Martial**

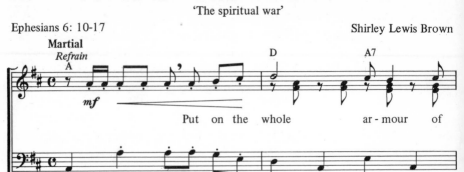

Put on the whole ar - mour of

God, put on the whole ar-mour of God, put on the

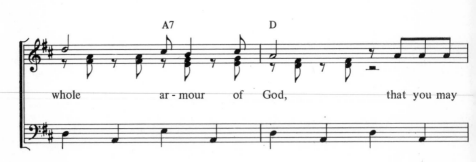

whole ar - mour of God, that you may

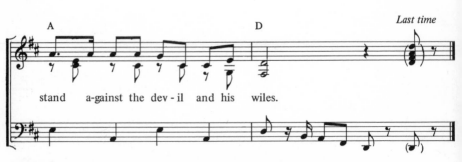

stand a-gainst the dev - il and his wiles.

A

1. Take your stand___ with truth as your belt.___
2. Put on right-eous- ness___ for your___ breast - plate.___
3. Shoe your feet___ with the gos - pel of peace.___
4. As your hel - met don sal - va - tion from God.___
5. In your hand___ take the sword of the Spi - rit,
6. A - bove all else___ take the shield of___ faith___ to

E

A

Take your___ stand___ with truth as your belt.___
Put on___ right-eous - ness___ for your___ breast - plate.___
Shoe your___ feet___ with the gos - pel of peace.___
As your___ hel - met don sal - va - tion from God.___
Which is ___ real - ly___ the word of___ God.___
quench all the fier - - - y___ darts of the wick - ed.___

A7                    D

___ Put on the whole ar- mour of

## 94. Clean hands

Capo 1 (E)

'Bethany'
Lowell Mason
*Arr.* Betty Pulkingham

Author unknown

**Simply**

Clean hands or dirt-y hands, brown eyes or blue, pale cheeks or ro-sy cheeks, Je-sus loves you. Come to him while you may, be his lit-tle lambs to-day. Clean hands or dirt-y hands, Je-sus loves you.

# Bless you, Jesus

**95.**

Robert Reynolds

Other verses may be added:
Love you.......... Trust you....... Serve you....... Praise you.......

*Last verse:*
Amen, Jesus, Amen. *(repeat twice).*
All the people now say, 'Amen.'
*(spoken)*

## 96. He's my rock, my sword, my shield

Author unknown
*Verse 2:* Wendy Rhodes

Composer unknown
*Arr.* Jeanne Harper

1. He's my rock, my sword, my shield, He's the wheel in the mid-dle of the wheel; He's the li - ly of the val - ley the bright and morn-ing star. Makes no differ - ence what you say, I'm go-ing on my knees and pray, I'm gon-na see my Lord in glo - ry one of these

2. He's my peace, my joy, my love, My name's written in his book a - bove, He's the cap-tain of my company in the bat - tle of the Lord. Makes no difference what the devil may do, I've got vic-try, how a-bout you? I'm gon-na see my Lord in glo - ry one of these

SECTION 8

# GO FORTH!

### SONGS OF OUTREACH

97.

# Prayer of St. Francis

Sebastian Temple
*Arr.* Betty Pulkingham

where there's doubt, true faith—— in—— you. ——
where there's sad - ness, ev - er—— joy. ——
dy - ing that we're born to e-ter-nal life. ——

Oh,

mas - ter, grant that I may nev - er seek ——

so

much to be con - soled as to con - sole; ——

to be

un - der-stood as to un - der - stand; ——

to be

loved, as to love with all my soul. ——

* Voices may sing in two-part harmony.

## 98.  The light of Christ

Donald Fishel
*Arr.* Betty Pulkingham

**Flowing**

*Refrain*

**Part 1.** The light of Christ has come in - to the world, the light of Christ has come in - to the world.

**Part 2.** The light of Christ has come in - to the world, the light of Christ has come.

*Verses*

1. All men must be— born a-gain to— see the king-dom of
2. God gave up his— on-ly Son out of love— for the
3. The light of God has— come to us so that we might have sal-

God; the— wa-ter and the— Spi-rit bring new—
world, so that all— men who be-lieve in him will—
va-tion; from the dark-ness of our— sins we walk in-to

life— in God's love.—
live— for— ev-er. world.
glo-ry with Christ Je-sus.

## 99. Drop everything and go

Diane Davis

**It** makes no dif - fer - ence who you are. It makes no dif - fer - ence where you're go - ing to; when Je - sus calls to you, drop ev'ry-thing and go, drop ev'ry-thing and go.

1. Pe - ter was_ a fish - er - man, he____ was fish-ing in his
2. Laz' - rus was dead and__ bound, dead__ and bound in his
3. Je - sus is__ the Son of__ God, his Fa - ther called un - to

boat._____ When__ Je - sus called__ to__
grave._____ When__ Je - sus called__ to__
him,_____ said, 'My peo - ple _____ need to be re-

him, he dropped ev'- ry-thing and he went, _____ he
him, he dropped all his bonds and he went, _____ he
deemed.' He took up his cross and he went _____ to

dropped ev'- ry-thing and he went.
dropped all his bonds and he went.
die for__ you and__ me.

## 100. Let there be peace on earth

Sy Miller and Jill Jackson

Let there be peace on earth and let it be-
Let peace be - gin with me, let this be the

gin with me; ___ Let there be peace on
mo - ment now. ___ With ev' - ry step I

earth, the peace that was meant to be, ___ With
take, let this be my sol - emn vow: ___ To

God as our Fa - ther, ___ bro - thers all are

we, \_\_\_\_\_ Let me walk with my bro - ther \_\_\_\_\_ in per - fect har - mo ny. \_\_\_\_\_ take each mo-ment and live each mo-ment in peace e- ter - nal - ly. \_\_\_\_\_ Let there be peace on earth and let it be - gin with me. \_\_\_\_\_

**101.**

# Freely, freely

Carol Owens

share his love as he told me to. }
share his pow'r as he told me to. } He said

*Refrain a tempo*

free - ly, free - ly you have re - ceived;

free - ly, free - ly give. ___

Go in my name and be - cause you be - lieve,

oth - ers will know that I live. ___ 2. All ___

* For variation, some voices may sing in thirds above the refrain melody, like this:

etc.

# The Spirit is a-movin'

102.

Carey Landry

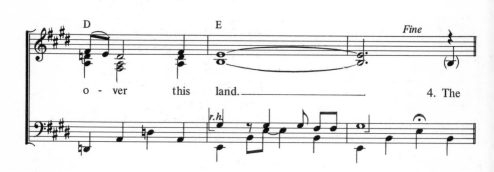

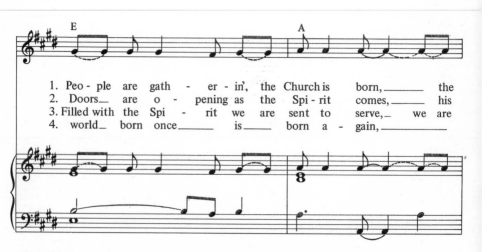

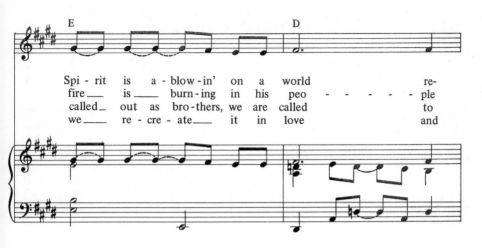

Spi - rit is a - blow - in' on a world re-
fire____ is ____ burn - ing in his peo - - - - - ple
called__ out as bro - thers, we are called to
we ____ re - cre - ate__ it in love and

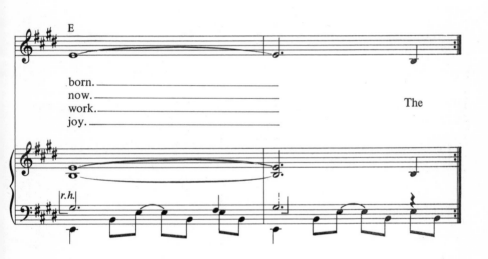

.born._____
now._____
work._____     The
joy. _____

5.  Old men are dreaming dreams,
    And young men see the light.

6.  Old Walls are falling down,
    And men are speaking with each other.

7.  The Spirit fills us with his power
    To be his witnesses to all we meet.

8.  The Spirit urges us to travel light
    To be men of courage who spread his fire.

9.  God has poured out his Spirit
    On all, on all of mankind.

# 103.

# Moto Imeaka

East African folk song
*Arr.* Betty Pulkingham

Capo 1 (E)

**Full and free**

im - be Hal - le - lu - jah, Mo - to im - ea - ka.    1. God's
God. I've got God's fire    and it's burn-ing in my soul.    (Refrain)

*This song in Swahili is sung throughout East Africa. The literal English translation of the refrain is: 'The fire is burning today, fire is the work of Jesus, the fire is burn-ing today, let us sing Hallelujah, the fire is burning.' The English verse in the musical text has essentially the same meaning. Other suggested verses: 'God's Spirit is burn-ing.....','God's power is burning.....'. The last line may be repeated accumulatively, in reverse order: 'Praise God I've got God's Spirit.....', 'power.....', 'fire.'

## 104.    And ye shall have power

Acts 1: 6-8

Clive Corrin
*Arr.* Betty Pulkingham

**With a lilt**

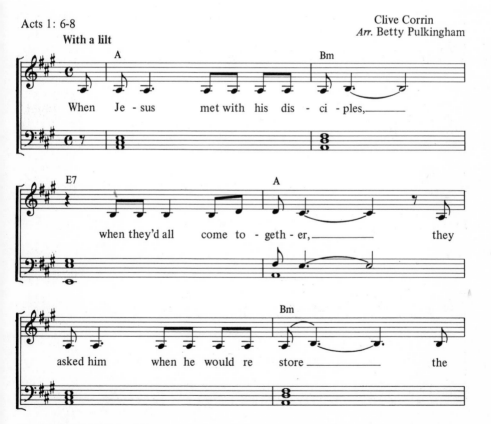

When Je - sus    met with his dis - ci - ples,_____

when they'd all    come to - geth - er,_____    they

asked him    when he would re store _____    the

king - dom _____ of Is - rael. ___

He told them that the time _____ was

not for them to know, the

times and the sea - sons were his Fa - ther's,

on - ly he would know.

*But ye shall have pow'r _____

to the ends of the earth.

to the ends of the earth.'

## 105. Come to the waters

Jodi Page

With a gentle swing

Come to the wa - ters and

I will give you rest.
you will be re - freshed.

1. Je - sus said, _____ 'Come un - to
2. Je - sus said _____ of the wa - ters
3. Je - sus said, _____ 'He who be-
4. So with joy _____ ye shall draw

me _____ all ye wea - - - - - - - -
that he gave, he who drinks _____
lieves in me out of him shall
wa - ter out of wells _____

- - - ry, hea - vy la - den.' _____
____ shall nev - er thirst a - gain. _____
flow liv - ing wa - ters.' _____
_____ of sal - va - tion. _____

D.C.

## 106. Jesus! the name high over all

'Lydia'
Thomas Phillips

Charles Wesley
**With strength**

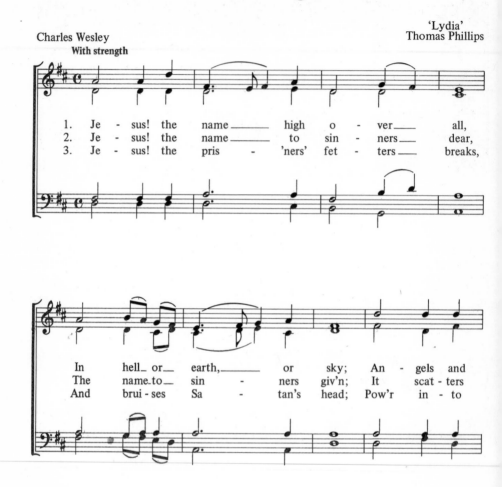

1. Je - sus! the name____ high o - ver____ all,
2. Je - sus! the name____ to sin - ners____ dear,
3. Je - sus! the pris - 'ners' fet - ters____ breaks,

In hell_ or_ earth,____ or sky; An - gels and
The name to_ sin - ners giv'n; It scat - ters
And brui - ses Sa - tan's head; Pow'r in - to

men be - fore it fall,____ And de - vils fear and
all their guil - ty fear,____ It turns their hell to
strength-less souls it speaks, ____ And life in - to the

fly, _____ And de - vils __ fear__ and__ fly.
heav'n, _____ It turns__ their__ hell __ to __ heav'n.
dead, _____ And life__ in - to __ the __ dead.

4.   O that the world might taste and see
       The riches of his grace;
     The arms of love that compass me
       Would all mankind embrace. *(repeat)*

5.   His only righteousness I show,
       His saving grace proclaim;
     'Tis all my business here below
       To cry: 'Behold the lamb!' *(repeat)*

6.   Happy, if with my latest breath
       I might but gasp his name;
     Preach him to all, and cry in death;
       'Behold, behold the lamb!' *(repeat)*

**107.**

# The Spirit of the Lord

Isaiah 61: 1-2

Jim Strathdee

The Spi-rit of the Lord is up-on me, because he has a-noint-ed me to
preach good news to the poor. He has
sent me to pro-claim re-lease to the cap-tives and re-
cov-er-ing of sight to the blind,
to set at lib-er-ty those who are op-press-ed, to pro-
claim the ac-cept-a-ble year of the Lord.

*May be sung without accompaniment, antiphonally:* the leader sings a phrase, the people repeat it, and this pattern continues throughout the seven musical phrases of the song (marked*). Then all sing the song without the repeats.

## 108.

# Come follow me now

Capo 1 (E)

Anna Withey
*(age 10)*

**Simple and unhurried**

Come fol-low me now, come fol-low me now, come fol-low me
now, said Je - sus. 1. He died on the cross and
2. I share my bo - dy with the

bore all our pain. I walk in his love, and he sends the
whole of the world; if you drink of my blood, you will live ev - er-

rain to wa - ter the plants that he gives to us. And
more. So fol - low me now, go tell the good news that

I do know he loves us. Come Je - - sus.
Christ is liv - ing in us.

# Topical Index

# Choirmaster's Guide

The following songs are appropriate for *CHOIRS*

The following songs have verses which may be sung as *SOLOS*
or by *SOLO ENSEMBLES*

# Index of titles and first lines

*The first line of a song is included, in italic type, only where it differs from the title*